MW00949076

8-1-7363371-0-3
363371-2-7

C. Ayers
Dr. Amber Langshaw
n Illustrator
n Illustrator

SOPHIE STRONG

A Little Girl with
Inflammatory Bowel Disease

By
Randi B. Rosen

Copyrigl

All rights
or used in
except for tl

To request pe

Hardcover: 97
Ebook: 978-1-7

Edited by Nicole
Medical Advisor:
Cover art by Arsala
Illustrator by Arsala

Dedication Page

This book is dedicated to my daughters.

To my amazing daughter Saige Parker Rosen. At two years old, she was diagnosed with Ulcerative Colitis.

She has taught me to stay strong and be brave. There is a superhero inside all of us who can fight

anything! This is for you, Superhero Saige.

To my wonderful daughter Jorie Blake Rosen. Thank you for being my alpha reader and trusted advisor. I

couldn't have written this book without you.

SOPHIE STRONG
A LITTLE GIRL WITH
INFLAMMATORY BOWEL DISEASE

Introducing Inflammatory bowel diseases, such as Ulcerative Colitis and Crohn's, to young children

By
Randi B. Rosen

Sophie was a five-year-old little girl. She lived with her mom, dad, and big sister Izzy. She also had a cute dog named Taffy.

Sophie was super silly and loved to laugh. She swam, played tennis, created art, and cuddled her favorite lovey, Bibby the Bunny.

Most of all, Sophie loved to dance! She dreamed about becoming a ballerina when she grew up.

One day, Sophie started having bad bellyaches and sometimes complained her tushy hurt.

Sophie had to go to the potty a lot and made more poopy than usual. Sophie's mommy noticed a little blood in the potty, which made her worried. She made Sophie a doctor's appointment.

Sophie wanted her tummy and tushy to feel better.

Sophie and her parents went to visit a special tummy doctor, Dr. Lang. Dr. Lang pushed on Sophie's belly, which made her giggle.

Dr. Lang said she was going to order some exams to see what was going on in Sophie's body. She wanted to keep Sophie healthy and strong.

A few days later, Sophie and her parents met Dr. Lang at the hospital. Sophie put on a special nightgown and laid down in a bed. A nurse took Sophie's temperature and put a funny cuff around her arm that gave her arm a gentle squeeze. She also put a small box on Sophie's finger that showed her how Sophie was breathing. It was all very easy and didn't hurt.

The nurse said Sophie was brave and called her Sophie Strong!

Dr. Lang came into Sophie's Room. She told Sophie a nice Doctor was going to come in and give Sophie some medicine that would make her sleepy. Then Dr. Lang would do her exam. Bibby the Bunny would cuddle Sophie the entire time.

While Sophie was asleep, Dr. Lang did tests to see why Sophie was having bellyaches. When Sophie woke up, she saw her mom, dad, and Bibby the Bunny. Sophie was home in time for dinner.

Sophie and her parents went to see Dr. Lang again. Dr. Lang told Sophie she had a condition called ulcerative colitis, or UC. She told Sophie to imagine that her body created little red circles inside that gave her bellyaches and made her go to the potty a lot.

The good news was there were a few things Sophie could do to help those circles get smaller and to help her body feel better.

First, Sophie had to eat colorful veggies and fruits that made her plate look like a rainbow. She got to play with new recipes in the kitchen with her mommy.

Sophie could also do a lot of fun activities to move her body and stay healthy, like take lots of dance classes.

There were special medicines Sophie could take as well. Some medicines could be taken at home, but some Sophie would have to get from a nurse or doctor.

Sophie and her parents went to the treatment center. They walked into a room and saw many other kids getting a similar medicine. Sophie sat in a comfortable chair with a blanket, her tablet, and Bibby.

Sophie had to get a prick in her arm for this medicine, but she remembered she was Sophie Strong, a very brave girl!

Sophie relaxed in her chair and watched a movie on her tablet for a couple of hours, and then she went home.

As Sophie grew up, she continued taking her medicine, which helped keep her body healthy and strong.

Sophie lived a fun-filled life. She went to sleepaway camp, enjoyed family vacations, played lots of sports, and went to college.

When Sophie was older, she became a mommy too.

The best news of all, Sophie's dream came true!
SOPHIE STRONG grew up and became a
prima ballerina!

Note to Readers

Dear Reader,

In March 2020, I noticed my two-year-old daughter had some rectal bleeding, which led to many doctor visits and an official diagnosis of ulcerative colitis. We were all in shock because she was so young. She showed no other symptoms, and we have no family history of inflammatory bowel disease, or IBD.

I became a mom on a mission. I spoke with doctors around the world from the University of Miami, Mayo Clinic, Boston's Children's Hospital, and Children's Hospital of Pennsylvania to name a few. I took my daughter to see a naturopathic doctor. I also connected with parents of other children with a similar disease.

I've learned my family is not alone in having a young child with IBD. What my daughter has is considered VEO-IBD (Very Early Onset Inflammatory Bowel Disease), which is becoming more and more common with children under the age of six.

I also found out that there isn't much information for parents about VEO-IBD. Most ulcerative colitis & Crohn's patients are ten and older when diagnosed.

I'm not a doctor. I am not one to give any medical advice to parents or tell people how to handle these conditions. I am just a mom who thought it would help to have a book to share with young kids who go through this. It was hard to explain to my toddler why she had to see the doctor a lot, get exams, and take medication daily. My hope is that this book can help guide other parents on this journey.

Sincerely, Randi

A portion of proceeds from book sales will be donated to the Crohn's and Colitis foundation.

(Narrative is from their website)
The Crohn's and Colitis Foundation is a non-profit, volunteer-fueled organization dedicated to finding the cures for Crohn's disease and Ulcerative Colitis, and to improving the quality of the life of children and adults affected by these diseases. It was founded in 1967 by Irwin M. and Suzanne Rosenthal, William D. and Shelby Modell, and Henry D. Janowitz, M.D.

To find out more information, please visit: http://www.crohnscolitisfoundation.org

Acknowledgments

Thank you to the following people for their support and love:

Austin Rosen for always being my rock and believing in me, Jorie Blake Rosen, Stuart and Susan Rosenholtz, Dr. Richard and JoAnn Chaset, David Rosenholtz, Corey Rosenholtz, Rachel and Linda Behar, Marla Rosen, Damien Rosen, Dr. Ivette Cardelli, close friends, and all of Saige's teachers. Huge thanks to Dr. Amber Langshaw and the Pediatric Gastroenterology Unit at the University of Miami.

About the Author

Randi B. Rosen's journey in life has taken her from being an actress, theater director, photographer and now a published author. She resides in South Florida with her husband, Austin, and her two greatest creations daughters, Jorie and Saige.